Tiger's Di

By Janice Pimm

Illustrations by Jon Stuart

OXFORD

UNIVERSITY PRESS

In this story ...

💬 TALK

- Introduce children to the characters in this story: Cat and Tiger.
- Point to the words that represent the characters' names and say each of the names together. Children will meet these words in the story.

Cat

Tiger

📖 READ

Cat and Tiger have special watches. When they push the buttons on their watches they can shrink to micro-size, like this …

1

2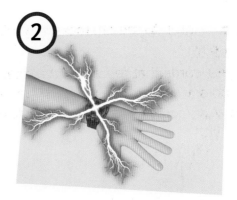

3

They become tiny and can have amazing adventures!

📖 READ

It was a bright, sunny day. Cat and Tiger were relaxing in the garden. Cat was having a nap.

"I'm too hot!" moaned Tiger.

Cat opened one eye lazily. "Have a sip of water," she said.

💬 TALK

- What are Cat and Tiger doing in the garden?
- Why might Tiger be thirsty?

👥 ACTIVITY

- Say the word *day* and ask children to repeat it. What sound does the word *day* begin with? Remember to use the *sound* of the letter, not the letter name.
- Ask children to spot other objects in the picture that begin with the /d/ sound (e.g. dish, daffodil).

⭐ Tip

See the inside back cover for more guidance on sounds.

Tiger sips. Cat naps.

📖 READ

"I'm still too hot," Tiger moaned again.

Cat sat up and began to munch the last few crisps. Then she had an idea.

"We can make a micro-sized paddling pool!" she said. "Let's tip my water into the dish."

💬 TALK

- Ask children if they have ever played in a paddling pool. If not, ask them to imagine what it might be like.

👥 ACTIVITY

- Point to the word *tip* on the page and ask children to sound-talk it (i.e. tip becomes t-i-p).
- Then ask children to blend the sounds together and say the word (i.e. t-i-p becomes tip).
- Can they find the other word with *tip* in it on the page? (tips)

Tip it in, Cat.

Cat tips it in.

📖 READ

Cat and Tiger pushed the buttons on their watches to shrink to micro-size.

The paddling pool looked nice and cool.

"Dip your toe in!" said Cat.

Tiger put his foot in the water … and pulled it straight out again! "Argh!" he yelped. The water was *freezing*.

💬 TALK

- Why is the water so cold?

👥 ACTIVITY

- Point to the word *dip* on the page and ask children to sound-talk it (i.e. dip becomes d-i-p). Ask children to pretend to dip their toes into water as they say each sound.
- Then ask children to blend the sounds together and say the word (i.e. d-i-p becomes dip).

Dip it in, Tiger.

8

READ

"You knew it would be cold!" grumbled Tiger.

Cat giggled. "It's just the ice cubes from my drink," she said.

Tiger frowned.

"Don't be mad with me!" said Cat. "The sun will soon melt the ice cubes. Then we can play."

💬 TALK

- Ask children why they think Tiger is mad at Cat.
- How do they think the story will end?

Tiger is mad at Cat.

The children waited and the sun melted the ice.

Tiger dipped his feet in the warm water, splashing Cat. Cat laughed and splashed him back.

"This was a great idea, Cat!" said Tiger.

- Ask children how they think Cat and Tiger feel now.

Tiger dips in.